Published by:
A Child's Voice
P.O. Box 550
Arlington Heights, IL 60006

Phone: 847-797-0625
www.poeticclassroom.com

First Edition
Bill Buczinsky

Strange World / by Bill Buczinsky;
Illustrated by Jeane L. Heckert
VisionMaker Graphics
80 p. Journal

Summary: a collection of poems, quotes and
prompts to inspire children of all ages to discover and
develop their poetic powers.

ISBN 978-0-9798283-0-0

November, 2016

For Billy

You might as well admit it. You've felt it
for awhile. Go ahead and say it, no
need to try to hide it.

You are strange!

You have your own way of seeing things,
your own way of doing things, your own
wild way of sailing through the world.
Go ahead, admit it —

You are really strange!

And it's about time you *celebrate* it!

This journal is a place to celebrate your strangeness. It's a place for all the weird ideas buzzing in your brain. It's a place to draw funny pictures, and tell out-of-this-world stories. A place for freaky characters and alien expressions. Or maybe just a place for your simple thoughts and quiet feelings. This book is yours to create.

Throughout the book you'll find some poems, some quotes and some questions to guide you on your own poetic journey.

Now, go ahead ... be strange!

"Life ain't lived in a straight-backed chair!"

– Bill Buczinsky

Slip!
Slop!
Slurp!

If you want to write a poem,
Put some words in your mouth.
Roll them around like gumballs.
Roll them around on your tongue.
You might take a sip to moisten your lips,
Don't be afraid to work up a little spit.

And when you say:
Slurp! Slop! Slip!

Words will begin to drip.
Open your mouth, words will come out.
And that's how a poem begins.

With the flip of a fin, a fish will swim. Where would you swim if your feet were fins?

The Mad Scientist

The Mad Scientist isn't mad at all,
In fact, he's insanely happy!
With his beakers bubbling, electricity flying –
Life is an experiment and the fun is in trying.

Pour some gunk in a petri dish,
Atoms collide, molecules miss.
Watch out for the bang and the hiss!
Where did it start? When will it end?
Light, time and a mind can bend.

The Mad Scientist isn't mad at all,
In fact, he's insanely happy!
From Einstein to Edison,
From robotics to medicine,

From botany to astronomy to nanomicrobiology —
Analyzing, synthesizing, hypothesizing, categorizing —
It's not madness in his eyes you're seeing,
It's the wonder, awe and surprise of being!

So let him be to his bubbling beakers;
His microscope, test tubes and little lab creatures.
And on your way out, before you say goodbye,
Turn on the switch, and turn it up high.
Don't be afraid when the sparks start flying —

Life is an experiment and the fun is in trying.

"Anything
is possible.
Anything can be."

–Shel Silverstein

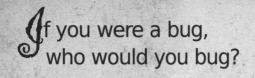 

If you were a bug,
who would you bug?

_____

_____

_____

_____

_____

_____

_____

_____

_____

_____

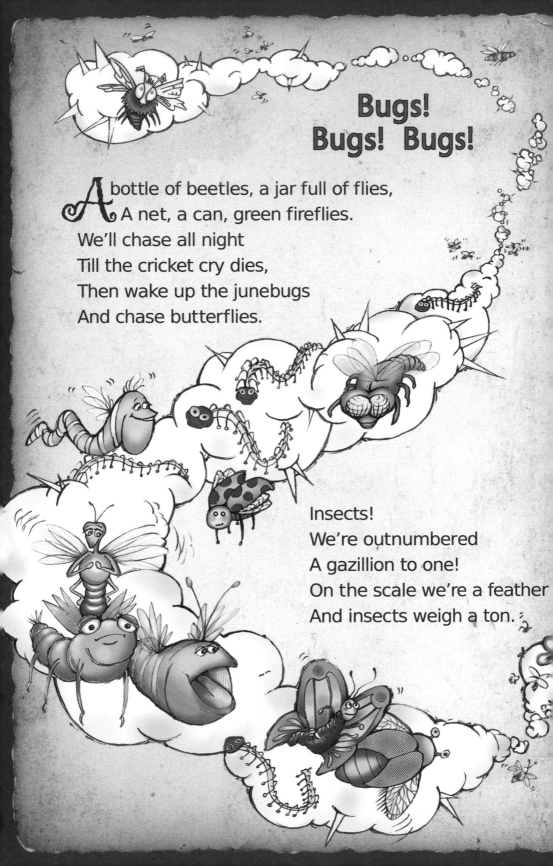

Bugs!
Bugs! Bugs!

A bottle of beetles, a jar full of flies,
A net, a can, green fireflies.
We'll chase all night
Till the cricket cry dies,
Then wake up the junebugs
And chase butterflies.

Insects!
We're outnumbered
A gazillion to one!
On the scale we're a feather
And insects weigh a ton.

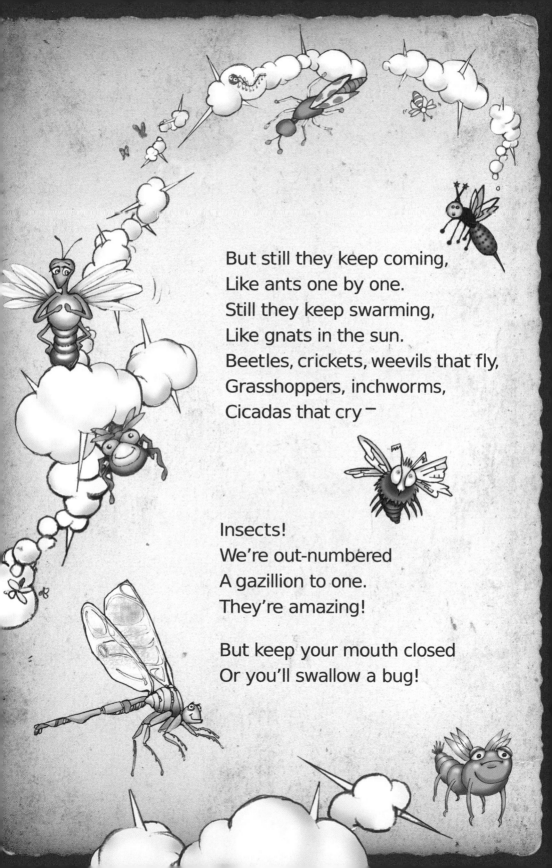

But still they keep coming,
Like ants one by one.
Still they keep swarming,
Like gnats in the sun.
Beetles, crickets, weevils that fly,
Grasshoppers, inchworms,
Cicadas that cry —

Insects!
We're out-numbered
A gazillion to one.
They're amazing!

But keep your mouth closed
Or you'll swallow a bug!

"I dwell in possibility."

–Emily Dickinson

In metaphor masks
everyone asks,
what sort of something
can I be?

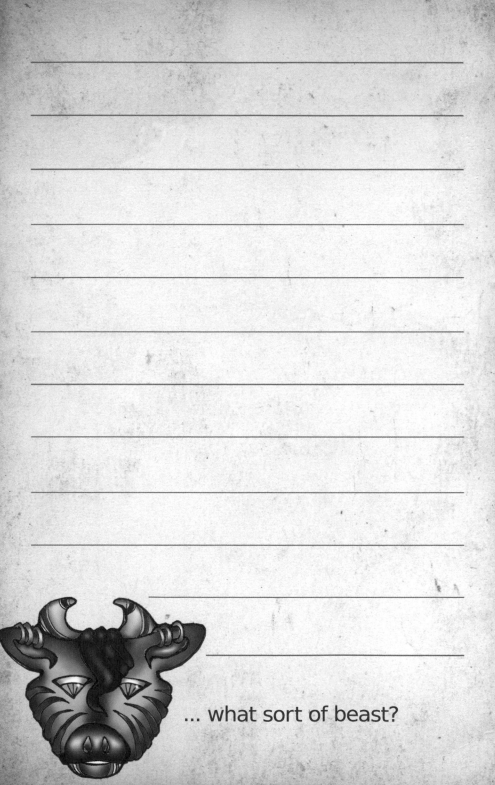

... what sort of beast?

... what sort of elf?

_____

_____

_____

_____

_____

_____

_____

_____

_____

_____

... what sort of something
can I be?

"I tilt my hat
anyway I choose."

– Walt Whitman

Wild! Awed! Attacked!

Wild! Awed! Attacked!
Following elephant tracks.
Wild went this way,
Awed went that,
Attacked went this way, that way and back.

Pachyderms pounding,
Elephant tusks,
Pounding and pounding,
The horn and the trunk.

Follow and follow,
If follow you must.
But when following elephants
Watch out —
For the big brown clumps!

What do you watch for
When you watch out,
When your senses are on safari,
And your wits are all about?

Wiggle Waggle

If a wiggle is what you got
Then waggle is what you do.
It's ten times fun as fine art
And tickles like a fiddler's shoe.

Just grab a free-flying heart
And faddle like the fiddlers do.
And your wiggle will always have waggle
And your poetry will always be true.

What is the flavor of a fairy's kiss?

_____

_____

_____

_____

_____

_____

_____

_____

_____

A Dream-Tied Balloon

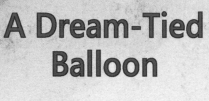

If your dream has too much sigh
You're not giving it enough balloon.
Just take one helium breath
Blow it to the sky.
Give it enough huff 'n puff
Aim it really high.

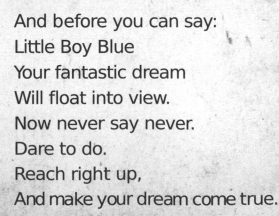

And before you can say:
Little Boy Blue
Your fantastic dream
Will float into view.
Now never say never.
Dare to do.
Reach right up,
And make your dream come true.

Slurp! Slop! Slip!
Words begin to drip.
Open your mouth, words will come out
and that's how a poem begins.

_____

_____

_____

_____

_____

_____

_____

_____

Magic in
the Air

Tinker Bell twinkles.
The Tooth Fairy shines.
The Godmother delivers
A dollar and a dime.

Some creatures reach you
With the tinkle of a chime.
Like a feather on your pillow.
Like and old-time nursery rhyme.

Like confetti when it flutters
Falling fast and falling fine,
There's magic in the air—
Open up your eyes.

"Life is an experiment.
The fun is in trying!"

– Bill Buczinsky

The Wizard

The wicked witch is dead.
Now we've got a wizard instead.
The bumbling fraud has no magic at all.
His machine is junk! The false fire and all.

Bring me a wizard with fire in his eyes,
With potions and spells that defy and mystify.
Who can turn a frog into a prince
And a dragon into a fly.
Then *Poof*! disappear
Right in front of your eyes.

Keep your weary wizard
With his carpetbag of tricks.
Keep his smoke and mirrors,
They're bound to make you sick!

And make my wizard
Out of magic, moon and castle mist.
Add the eye of newt,
A touch of toad to make it hiss.
Then stir in fire from heaven
And watch my wizard whiz!

He'll quench the scorch of the dragon
With one drop from his Holy Grail.
He'll terrorize the trolls,
Make the wicked witches wail.
He'll charm the ancient serpent,
Grab it by the tail,
Swing it round and round,
Make a whirlwind whirl!

So keep your country wizard
Promising rainbow skies.
Keep that Kansas wizard at home
Eating Aunt Em's pies.

And bring me a wizard
From old and ancient times.
Bring me a wizard
Who is fearless, free and wild!
You bring me a wizard
With fire in his eyes,
And I'll take that wizard home with me
And make that wizard mine.

"A little
innocence
creates a day."

– e.e. cummings

Bongo Billy

Bongo Billy beat the beatnik bongo.
Cool dude daddy-o, go man go!
Snap your fingers! Tap your feet!
Black beret, Billy was beat.

Drank haiku from the campfire stew.
Hitchhiked south with the Mexico blues.
Jump up! Jump back!
Went on the road with Jack Kerouac.

Slap him five. Come inside.
The joint is jumpin'!
The crowd is alive!
When Bongo Billy
Beats the beatnik bongos.

Cool dude daddy-o!
Go man go!

"Exuberance
is beauty."

– William Blake

King of Style

The look I like a lot
The fashion gods ain't got.
Ain't found in the seam
Of designer jeans,
Or the made-up eyes
In a magazine.

Just stand up straight and tall,
Look me straight in the face.
Give me a smile.
Now I see —
You've got a natural grace.

Ain't found in the ripple
Of a strong man's muscle.
The powdered pills
Are a scam and a hustle.

Ain't found in the slick
Of the blue hair goo.
The look ain't in the new hairdo.

Just stand up straight and tall,
Look me straight in the face.
Give me a smile.
Now I see —
You've got a natural grace.

"Be cool, not cold.
Grow young, not old."

– Bill Buczinsky

Strange World

I just got back from the strangest land
Where to be confused is to understand.
I found everything there terribly confusing.
The most serious people find everything amusing.
Workers work hard by being lazy,
And the sanest people are really crazy.
The government enforces the oddest rule:
To become a genius, you must act like a fool.
Beggars are rich and billionaires poor
'Cause nothing valuable is bought in a store.
And the oldest roads lead to the newest places,
Where the oldest souls have the youngest faces.

It really was a mixed-up town,
Topsy-turvy, upside down.
Heaven and earth were turned around,
So land was sky, and sky was ground.
While visiting there I was lost in space,
My wits had vanished without a trace.
My senses had done a complete about-face.
But when I got home
I sure missed that place.

About the strange creators.

*T*his book was created by two people who know a little something about being strange.

Bill Buczinsky is a children's poet, performer and teacher. He is the founder of *A Child's Voice,* a company that inspires young people of all ages to discover and develop their poetic powers. Bill likes to race aliens, howl at the moon and sleep under the stars. To book one of Bill's performances or teacher training workshops, contact *A Child's Voice*, P.O. Box 550, Arlington Heights, IL 60006 (847) 797-0625, or visit www.poeticclassroom.com.

Jeane Heckert is an illustrator and fine artist. She is the founder of *VisionMaker Graphics*, a company that brings people's visions to life. Jeane likes to soar with eagles, chatter with chipmunks and knit scarves for woodland creatures. For art and design services contact Jeane at visionmaker4hm@comcast.net, or call (847) 695-1321.